# Inspiration
## for Mostly Manuals

Kevin
Mayhew

We hope you enjoy the music in this book.
Further copies of this and other books in the series are available
from your local music shop or Christian bookshop.

In case of difficulty, please contact the publisher direct by writing to:

The Sales Department
KEVIN MAYHEW LTD
Buxhall
Stowmarket
Suffolk IP14 3BW

Phone 01449 737978
Fax 01449 737834
E-mail info@kevinmayhewltd.com

Please ask for our complete catalogue of outstanding Church Music.

First published in Great Britain in 1999 by Kevin Mayhew Ltd.

ISBN 1 84003 467 X
ISMN M 57004 618 8
Catalogue No: 1400220

0 1 2 3 4 5 6 7 8 9

Cover design by Jonathan Stroulger

Editor: Helen Goodall
Music Setter: Chris Mitchell

Printed and bound in Great Britain

# Contents

# IN THE SHADOW OF YOUR WINGS

## (Psalm 57: 1-6)

### Rosalie Bonighton

# WHERE SHALL I GO FROM YOUR SPIRIT?

(Psalm 139: 6-11)

Rosalie Bonighton

* *Fix with a pencil stub*
  *to hold throughout*

*Inspired by the codex of Robertsbridge Abbey*

# ROBERTSBRIDGE ABBEY

## Simon Clark

# PRELUDE

ANGELS, HELP US TO ADORE HIM, H. F. Lyte

Andrew Fletcher

15

# TOCCATA 2000

Andrew Fletcher

20

# COMMUNION PRELUDE

Michael Higgins

# MEDITATION

Michael Higgins

25

# PRELUDE ON A WELSH FOLKTUNE
(Bugeilio'r Gwenith Gwyn)

Robert Jones

26

*for NJCJ*

# TOCCATA

Robert Jones

# CLOISTER COURT

Richard Lloyd

poco rall.  a tempo

# NEAR MORDIFORD BRIDGE

Richard Lloyd

39

*for Peter and Emma*

# MEDITATION AT ENGELBERG

## John Marsh

# AN EVENT OF GREAT JOY

Colin Mawby

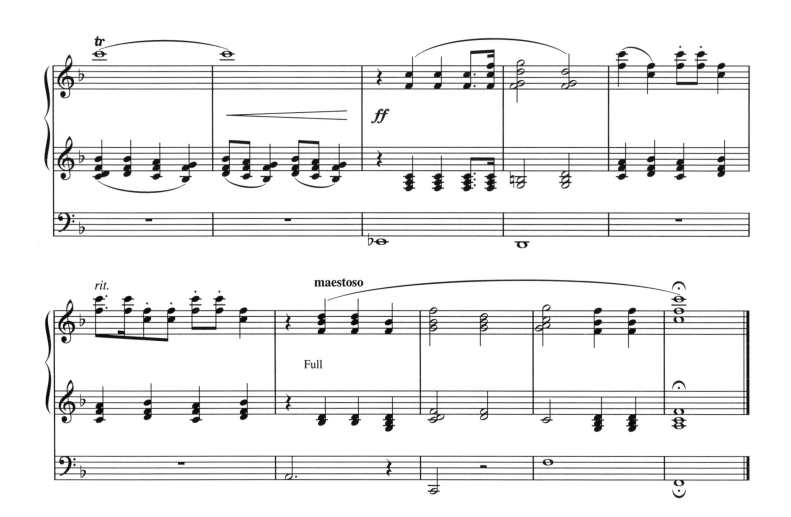

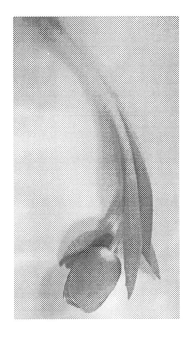

# REFLECTION AFTER TURMOIL

Colin Mawby

# HOMAGE TO SCARLATTI

Andrew Moore

51

# MALVERN AIR

Andrew Moore

55

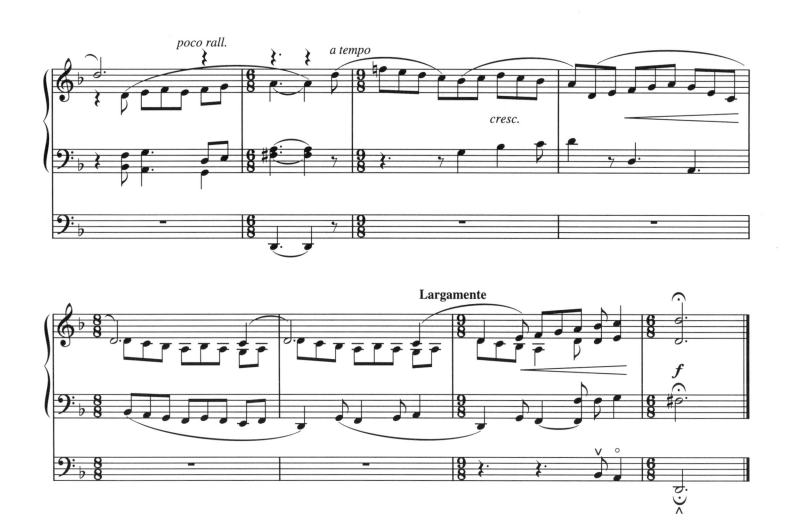

# JESU, GRANT ME THIS I PRAY

(Variations on Gibbons' Song 13)

June Nixon

Variation 2
Poco piu mosso ($\bullet$. = 76)

Variation 3
Alla sarabanda ($\bullet$ = 76)

Sw.
$p$

58

Variation 4

**Animato** ($\dot{\phantom{o}}$. = 66)

Sw. *mf*

Variation 5

**Sonoramente** (♩ = 72)

*mf*

*rit. e dim.*

*rall. e dim.*

Variation 6

**Lento** (♩ = 84)

Sw. *p*

61

*For Bishop James A. Grant*

# LIFT UP YOUR HEADS

## June Nixon